This book
belongs to

⌃⌃

A Monty Mouse
Adventure

BUILDING A HOUSE

Written by Glynis Holland
Adapted by Horace J. Elias

WATERTOWER BOOKS
DIVISION OF CHILDRENS PRESS

BUILDING A HOUSE

"My goodness!" exclaimed Mr. Preston P. Pig, "Look at that sign! This is just what I've been looking for! This will be the perfect place to build my new house by the seashore!"

Mr. Pig, as you can see, is very rich. He owns a sleek white speedboat, and a house in the city. But he also wants a house by the seashore that he can share with his good friends, Monty Mouse and Rapid Robert Rabbit.

"Let's go see Mr. Fred Fox right away!" he said to his friends.

"Well sir!" said Fred Fox. "So you want to buy my land to build a house, eh? That's wonderful!"

"That's exactly what I want, but first I need an architect to draw the plans for the house," replied Mr. Pig.

"Yes, indeed!" said Fred Fox. "Here is Bobby Bunny, the best in the business, at your service! He has all the right tools; a ruler, pencils and a T-square. He doesn't even stop working to eat lunch. He keeps his carrots right in the drawer!"

It isn't easy to build a house. A great many things can go wrong, as Preston P. Pig was to learn before his house was finished.

All sorts of different materials are used to build a house: wood, cement, bricks, nails, plaster and tiles for the roof. And all sorts of workmen have to be on hand, ready to make all those different things into the correct sizes and shapes, so that everything fits and works.

The workmen are doing the first thing that must be done before building can start. First a big tractor, with the heavy blade on the front, must clear and level the ground so that the workmen will have a flat surface to build on. Then the house will be level, too. Chris Cat's using a big drill to break up the hard-packed dirt and stones. Between the racket from the drill and from the tractor, Monty Mouse has to put his paws over his ears to keep out the noise!

Down in the corner, it looks as though someone is starting to dig a hole in the ground. He is being closely watched by a worm, who probably hates the whole thing!

After the hole is dug, it is time to build the foundation.

A house must have a strong foundation to give the workmen a firm base to build on.

In the top corner is Gideon Goat at the cement mixer. Fresh, gooey cement is needed to hold the bricks together.

The rabbits were hired to lay the bricks because they move very quickly. Their part of the job is done in a hurry!

Monty Mouse wants to help, but that trowel he's holding is bigger than he is! He'd be better off just watching and staying out of trouble. That's probably too much to ask of a playful mouse!

Now things are beginning to hum. Trucks are arriving with more material. You can see pipes for the plumbing and lumber for the doorways, floors and roof frame. Before long, the traffic will begin to pile up if someone doesn't take charge!

The take-charge-man is right there, though, making sure everything goes where it's supposed to go and no one gets mixed up. He's the one with the hard hat, pointing the way to the driver of the big truckload of lumber.

More cement, heavy pipes for the sewer lines, bricks and tiles...everything neat and orderly, except...

Yes, that's Mr. Preston P. Pig. He's so excited about his new house that he's decided to help by driving a dump truck full of sand. Poor Monty Mouse, who just wanted to play in the sandpile, is going to be covered over if Mr. Pig dumps his load of sand there! Maybe Mr. Pig will hear Monty shouting, "Don't dump it here. please!"

The house begins to take shape. The workmen "rough in" the door frames. The window frames will come next. Then they'll lay the bricks around the frames so that everything fits perfectly. Fred Fox is there to lend a hand, reading the plans to make sure everything's where it should be.

Someone who *isn't* where he should be is Monty Mouse! When Sylvan Squirrel sawed through a piece of wood, Monty found himself on a surprise sliding board. Hope he can swim! That bucket of water looks deep for a tiny mouse!

Do you see what's happening on this page? Donald Dog with his portable drill, and Chris Cat with his hammer and nails, are putting the roof frame together. They must be very careful, so that the roof tiles will fit on the frame.

Donald and Chris had better not hammer or drill *too* hard! A certain mouse, who can't seem to stop playing dangerous games, is going to be a *flying* mouse, if that beam he's balancing on starts to shake!

Working side by side are Horace Hedgehog and his helper, Henry. Horace is an expert roofer, and he has one very important job to do. The roof tiles must fit perfectly, with no spaces in between to let in water. Horace is doing the fitting very carefully, so the roof will not leak in the heaviest rainstorm or snowfall.

Monty's in a very good spot to watch what's going on. Now how do you suppose he got there?

Of all the things that go into a house, electricity is one of the most important. It makes the lights go on, the refrigerator keep things cold, the kitchen stove keep things hot, the washing machine get things clean; and it makes the television give us fun things to watch. There are lots of control boxes, plugs and wires. Monty has managed to get himself tangled in one of the heavy wires.

Now it's time for the plasterers to go to work, spreading the wet, runny plaster to cover the rough walls. The plaster goes on wet; but it dries to a smooth, hard finish.

Preston P. Pig has somehow managed to slip and fall into a pile of the wet plaster! It's not a friendly thing to laugh when someone has an accident, but Monty Mouse can't help laughing!

Guess who's going to be laughing next...when that big blob of plaster lands smack dab on Monty's head!

Freddie Frog is supposed to be a very good plumber. He has to be, to connect all those water lines so that the hot water and cold water go through the right pipes to the right places! It could be very messy if the television set, or the kitchen stove, or the refrigerator, suddenly began spouting water!

But if Freddy Frog's such a good plumber, why is Monty Mouse getting all wet? Maybe Freddy's trying to wash the plaster off Monty!

Painting the inside of the house comes next. That's one of the reasons the plaster has to be put on so smoothly.

The painters don't seem to be very careful, do they? One of them is about to paint Preston P. Pig's nose! The one on the scaffolding has left a paint can tilted so it's going to start dripping on the floor, and the one on the ladder is dripping blobs of yellow down the wall!

Monty's not helping things much, either. He's made a great mess on the floor and on himself!

In spite of all the problems and all the trouble Monty Mouse and Preston P. Pig got into, the house is finally finished. It's a very handsome house, isn't it? It's right on the beach...with a driveway for Preston P. Pig's big automobile and a pretty white fence.

Preston P. Pig, Monty Mouse and Rapid Robert Rabbit seem to be very pleased with Fred Fox's work, and with the big golden key he's handing to the new owner.

To celebrate, Preston P. Pig decided to give a party for his friends and the people who worked so long and so hard on his house. Let's see! There's Fred Fox, and Freddie Frog the plumber, and Horace Hedgehog, and Donald Dog and Sylvan Squirrel. And of course, there's Rapid Robert Rabbit and Mr. Pig himself, and our funny friend, Monty Mouse.

That's probably the longest straw in the world that Monty's using to drink that soda pop! He deserves a reward for all the hard work he put into building that wonderful house by the sea...or at least for *trying* to help!

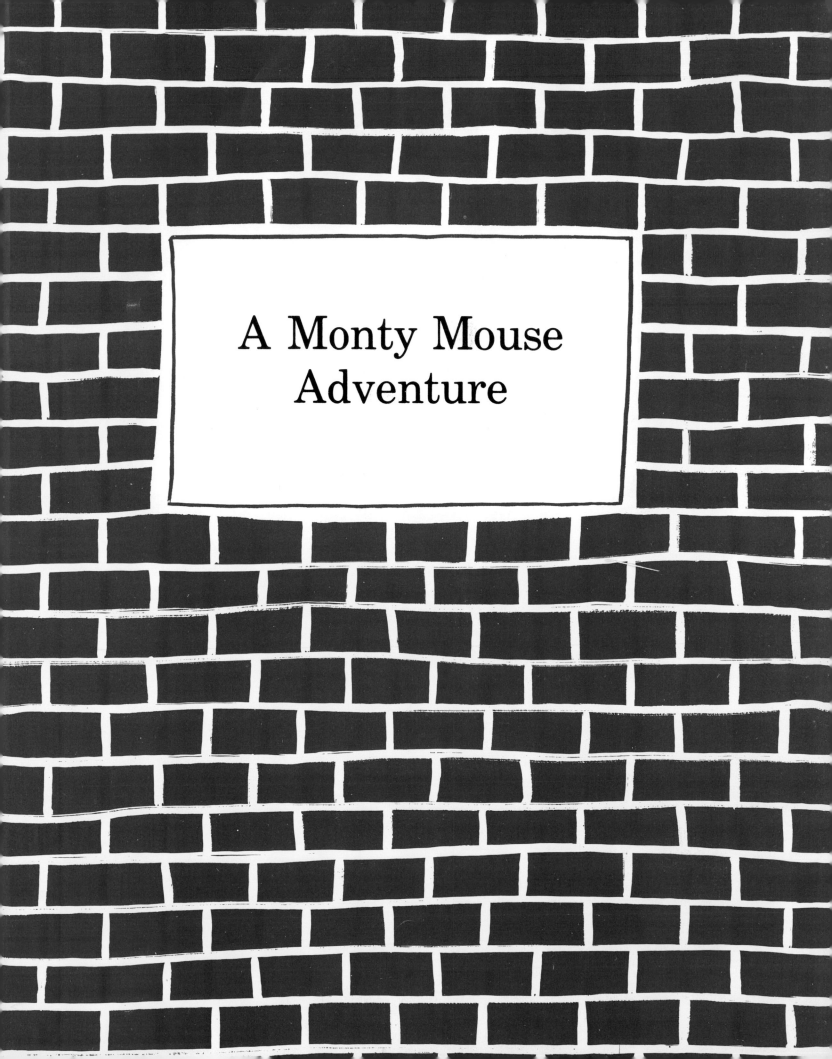

A Monty Mouse Adventure